Contents

© **Audit Commission 2004**

First published in March 2004 by the Audit Commission for local authorities and the National Health Service in England & Wales, 1st floor, Millbank Tower, Millbank, London SW1P 4HQ

Printed in the UK for the Audit Commission by Belmont Press

ISBN 186240 489 5

Photographs: Alamy (cover)

Summary

This study reviews primary care trusts' (PCTs') readiness to become proactive commissioners of primary care. It aims to help PCT managers to maximise the benefits of the new national contract with general practitioners (GPs) that will be implemented from April 2004, and which will be supported by additional planned investments of £1.9 billion in primary care for the UK.

The Audit Commission visited nine PCTs across England in mid 2003 collecting evidence of PCTs' arrangements for shaping general practice and data from practices. All PCTs were asked about their readiness for their new role in a national survey in October 2003 and a survey of 2,000 practice nurses was conducted with the help of the Royal College of Nursing.

Findings

Most PCTs were making progress to implement the new contract in late 2003, but capacity was stretched and some still lacked critical information.

- Most PCTs had agreed a work programme to implement the new contract and had taken some steps to improve their knowledge about practices, but some PCTs were ill-prepared on some issues.

- The capacity available to manage new relationships with practices varied considerably between PCTs, with finance capacity being particularly stretched.

Resources and services vary widely between general practices, with consequential wide variation in the value for money that they offer.

- In most study sites, the best resourced practices had over twice as much income per registered patient as the least well resourced practices. PCTs should use data generated by the implementation of the new contract and their local knowledge to understand the reasons why resources vary and devise ways to achieve equity.

- Actual consultations with GPs and nurses were consistently longer than planned, a discrepancy only partly explained by non-attendance of patients who had booked. PCTs should encourage practices to use the available incentives to improve the scheduling of appointments .

- The average ratio of whole time equivalent (wte) GPs to practice nurses was 2.4:1, with a range from 1:1 to 34.5:1; in 5 per cent of practices, practice nurses were not employed. This suggests scope for greater use of nurses in some practices.

Recommendations

For PCTs:

Improve the information base they use to make sound managerial decisions in order to tackle variations in resources and services between practices.

- PCTs must improve their understanding of the different levels of resources available to general practices and the way in which they are used, using the Audit Commission's benchmarking tool or another similar one.

- This information, and information about population health needs and patients' views, should then be used to develop strategies for commissioning and supporting primary care that will raise standards and deliver equity.

Improve accountability, information and access to the public.

- PCTs should seek to publish the achievements of practices in the quality and outcomes framework.

- They should ensure that all practice populations have access to disease management services that meet the standards set out in the national service frameworks (NSFs), commissioning such services from alternative providers where practices choose not to implement the quality and outcomes framework, or where they achieve very low standards and have no plans for improvement.

Ensure that there is sufficient capacity to commission and support primary care.

- PCTs should review the deployment of staff to primary care compared with other functions to ensure that sufficient capacity is available to secure the best value from primary medical services, and develop shared arrangements with other PCTs where appropriate.

For local auditors:

- Auditors should consider the level of PCT knowledge about general practice and capacity to implement the new contract when assessing the risks faced by each PCT and the way they are being managed.

- The management information that is routinely available to PCTs should be audited in order to ensure that they are in a position to fulfil their responsibility to provide services efficiently, effectively and economically.

For national bodies:

- The value for money and service improvement obtained through the expenditure of an additional £1.9 billion on the new primary medical services arrangements should be independently evaluated and assessed.

- The differential resourcing and provision of primary medical services between PCTs and between practices within PCTs should be addressed in implementing policies to improve choice and equity.

Introduction

1   This study reviews PCTs' readiness to become proactive commissioners of primary care. PCTs were set up in England between April 2000 and April 2002 to:

*   improve the health of the local population;

*   develop primary care; and

*   secure health services for their population.

The aim of the study is to help PCT managers to maximise the benefits from additional planned investments in primary care, new powers and the new national contract with general practices, to be implemented from April 2004. By using these changes to the full to develop primary care, PCTs will contribute to the achievement of their other two functions **(Exhibit 1)**.

Exhibit 1

PCT functions

By developing primary care PCTs will contribute to the achievement of all their goals.

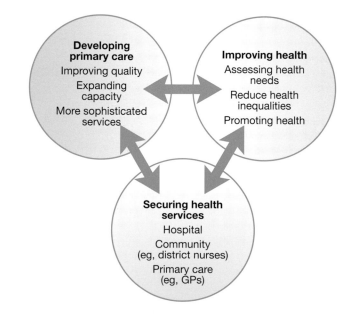

Source: Audit Commission

2   This study follows the Audit Commission's report, *A Focus on General Practice* **(Ref. 1)**, which presented an overview of the state of general practice in England. It found that, while general practice is a vital NHS service that has developed considerably since 1990 and is highly regarded by patients, it is also characterised by:

*   funding mechanisms that relate to the supply of doctors not health needs;

- inequitable variation in the breadth of services offered by practices;

- variations in the quality of services between practices; and

- critical elements of infrastructure – premises, information systems and practice management – that are largely dependent on individual practices, and that therefore also vary widely.

3 PCTs have a new duty to secure primary medical services **(Refs. 2 and 3)**. There are four contractual routes to obtain these: General Medical Services (GMS),[I] Personal Medical Services (PMSs),[II] alternative providers of primary medical services (APMS)[III] and PCT provided primary medical services (PCTMS).[VI] Existing GMS contractors have a right to a new GMS contract as long as they meet minimum statutory criteria. PMS contracts can continue. Significant investment in general practice is planned – an additional £1.9 billion in the UK in the three years to 2005/06. This is an average increase of 11 per cent per year in cash terms, which compares with the growth in PCT allocations[V] as a whole of 9.24 per cent in 2003/04, 9.55 per cent in 2004/05 and 9.32 per cent in 2005/06 **(Ref. 4)**.

4 The Audit Commission study team visited nine PCTs across England in the spring and summer of 2003. These PCTs included a range of sizes, geography, length of operation and range of practice size and types. Qualitative and quantitative evidence was collected on PCTs' arrangements for commissioning and supporting general practice services, and PCT staff were interviewed using a semi-structured interview. Data from practices were collected. Details of the methodology are given in Appendix 1. In September and October 2003, the team conducted a national survey of all 303 PCTs to identify progress towards implementation of the new GMS contract. In October 2003 a survey of 2,000 practice nurses was conducted, in collaboration with the Royal College of Nursing (RCN), to provide information about practice nurse roles, workforce issues and training and supervision arrangements.

5 In addition to this report, the Audit Commission has released a benchmarking tool to help PCTs to strengthen their knowledge of resource use in general practice and to assess their capacity. This is available at **www.audit-commission.gov.uk/pcts**

6 Chapter 1 of this report outlines the policy framework for primary care. Chapter 2 reports on PCTs' readiness for their new role in the second half of 2003, using evidence from study sites and the survey of PCTs and practice nurses. Chapter 3 reports on the contribution the Audit Commission's benchmarking tool can make to PCTs' knowledge base about practices, using data collected from more than 200 practices at nine study sites. Chapter 4 reports some examples of ways in which PCTs were tackling the challenges they face.

I The national contract for primary medical services agreed between the UK Governments and general practitioners.

II Locally negotiated contracts for primary medical services agreed between providers and PCTs.

III For example, not for profit organisations, commercial providers, NHS trusts, other PCTs.

IV The PCT in which the practice population lives providing personal medical services in particular by employing staff.

V PCTs receive allocations for all their functions calculated from their baseline expenditure compared with a needs based target allocation. PCTs that are under-resourced compared with their target allocation receive more growth than the minimum of 8.3 per cent in 2003/04, 8.88 per cent in 2004/05 and 8.49 per cent in 2005/06. By 2010 all PCTs should be receiving equitable allocations.

Policy framework

Background

7 Policies to improve health services are based on the principles of public sector reform:

- national standards for services;
- empowering frontline staff to design and deliver services;
- flexibility and responsiveness to meet individual need; and
- choice for users.

Organisationally, resources and power have been devolved to PCTs **(Ref. 5)**. The aim of policy relating to primary care services is to secure higher standards, thus reducing unacceptable variation, and to enable the development of a broader range of services, including substituting for hospital services where appropriate **(Refs. 6 and 7)**.

8 The new GMS contract sets out the standards that all GMS providers of primary medical services will have to meet. It has widespread support, in particular because it recognises the importance of:

- changing to needs-based funding of general practice;
- allowing practices to manage their own workload and enabling primary care professionals to exercise more flexibility and choice;
- including a quality framework which is evidence based and widely supported by doctors and others;
- retaining the strength of organising services for registered patients, enabling co-ordination and continuity of care;
- enabling expansion of primary medical services capacity; and
- guaranteed increases in investment.

Many of these features have been translated into revised PMS contracts.

Features of the new GMS contract

9 The new contract has three key elements that are supported by three funding streams – the global sum, the quality and outcomes framework and enhanced services **(Ref. 3)**. PCTs will, for the first time, need to agree a contract with each GMS practice based on the national agreement and Statement of Financial Entitlement.[I]

I The detailed agreement for payments to GMS practices, replacing the Statement of Fees and Allowances under the previous contract.

10 The global sum is calculated using a formula that describes the health needs of the registered practice population[I] and covers the activities that all practices must provide **(Exhibit 2)**. Practices may explicitly opt out of services, as shown. Where practices choose to do this, the PCT will deduct funds from the global sum and use the funds to secure those services for the practice population from another provider.

Exhibit 2

Key elements of the global sum

The global sum provides funding for the provision of essential primary medical services for patients and a range of non-patient activities, but practices can opt out of providing some patient services.

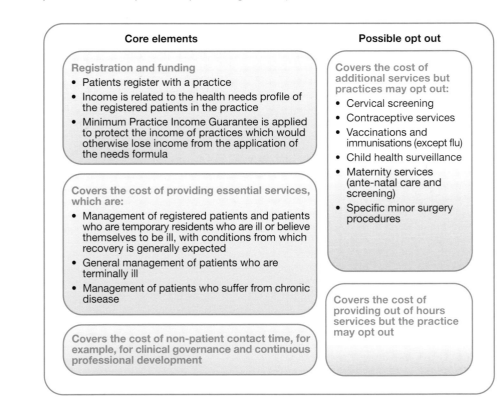

Source: Ref. 3

I   The formula will be adjusted as more reliable data become available. The global sum is estimated to be £300,000 in 2004/05 for an average practice with an average weighted population, or £53 per head of population **(Ref. 3)**.

11 A substantial proportion of practice income, in addition to the global sum, will be generated by achievement of quality standards in the quality and outcomes framework **(Exhibit 3)**. Achievement will be assessed against 146 evidence-based standards that generate 1,050 points if all are achieved. This is a voluntary system.

Exhibit 3

Key elements of the quality and outcomes framework

A proportion of practice income is generated by the achievement of quality standards.

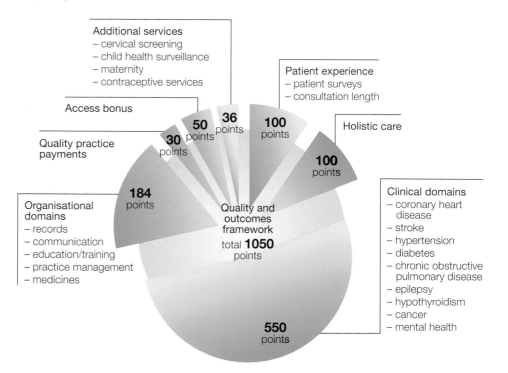

Note: Each point generates practice income of £75 in 2004/05 and £120 in 2005/06.

Source: Ref. 3

12 The third funding stream is enhanced services, defined as services other than essential, additional or out-of-hours **(Exhibit 4)**. These will be commissioned by PCTs and are expected to provide an opportunity to expand the breadth and complexity of work carried out by practices, some of which will substitute for work traditionally carried out by hospitals. All PCTs must spend a floor (or minimum) on local enhanced services, the amount of which will be specified annually in PCT allocations. They may spend more than this. The planning total for the floor is £315 million in 2003/04 and this will rise significantly by 2005/06 **(Ref. 4)**.

Exhibit 4
Enhanced services

Enhanced services are expected to enable the expansion of work carried out in primary care.

Locally Enhanced Services	Directed Enhanced Services	National Enhanced Services
For example: • More specialised services, for example, those provided by Practitioners with a Special Interest (PwSI) • Incentive schemes for secondary care referral management • Services addressing specific local needs • Piloting innovative services	• Improved access* • Childhood vaccinations* and immunisation target payments • Higher specification minor surgery** • Influenza vaccination for people 65 and over or at high risk** • Services for violent patients** • Quality information preparation*	National specifications and benchmark prices,*** for example: • Enhanced care of the homeless • Minor injury services • Specialised care of patients with depression • More specialised sexual health services

Notes:
*Must be available to GMS practices.
**Must be available within the PCT.
***Can be altered by local agreement.

Source: Audit Commission

PCT responsibilities

13 PCTs have significant strategic and operational responsibilities relating to primary medical services **(Box A, overleaf)**. In addition to the opportunities arising from the new contract, there are important national programmes for infrastructure improvement – workforce expansion and skill development, information systems and premises **(Refs. 8, 9, 10, 11 and 12)**. PCTs have a critical role to play in supporting practices to take advantage of these national programmes.

Box A

Key PCT responsibilities for primary medical services include:

- Managing the allocation for primary medical services and ensuring that the Gross Investment Guarantee[I] and enhanced services floor are achieved.

- Securing universal access to essential, additional and directed enhanced services.

- Ensuring that all patients can see a GP within 48 hours and a primary care professional within 24 hours.

- Securing primary medical services out-of-hours that meet national quality standards.

- Agreeing contracts with each practice, including those for additional and enhanced services where appropriate.

- Agreeing with each practice participating in the quality and outcomes framework their planned achievement level each year.

- Working with practices to avoid closure of their list to new patients and managing the consequences where closures are unavoidable.

- Running access support services and the access incentive scheme.

- Managing the prescribing budget.

- Supporting practices to improve the working lives and skills of practices' partners and staff.

- Funding and managing practice information systems, including ensuring full implementation of systems procured by the National Programme for Information Technology.[II]

- Ensuring the modernisation and expansion of the primary care estate, taking advantage of new flexibilities and funding mechanisms.

Source: Audit Commission

Risks associated with the new arrangements

14 The strategic risks of the new arrangements include:

- whether value for money can be achieved from the increased expenditure;

- whether sufficient professional staff can be attracted to, and retained in, general practice to sustain service expansion;

- how fair access and patient choice can be delivered, given the historic legacy of differential resourcing and service provision; and

I The guarantee that resources available for primary medical services, as agreed in the contract, are delivered. The guarantee will be monitored by a joint national committee of the Department of Health, NHS Confederation and profession, and strategic health authorities.

II The programme begun in 2002 to procure the hardware and software infrastructure necessary to implement the NHS strategy for information systems, Information for Health (Refs. 11 and 12).

- whether the shift of responsibility for out-of-hours primary medical services from GPs to PCTs can be managed at an affordable price, without destabilising services to the public or having an adverse impact on other emergency services.

15 The operational risks include:

- validating enhanced services and testing to ensure that they achieve value for money;

- establishing systems to secure accurate practice lists and reporting of quality achievements;

- seeking to ensure that practices with income protection[I] aspire to reach the highest possible standards in the quality and outcomes framework as early as possible; and

- supporting practices to manage failure to reach their planned level of achievement in the quality framework, which will result in lower than expected practice income, and participating in risk-sharing arrangements for practices that achieve higher standards than planned.[II]

[I] Where the global sum formula, which is needs based, does not deliver sufficient funds to match current practice income from essential services, practices will be protected by the Minimum Practice Income Guarantee. In England, it is estimated that 90 per cent of practices will receive the Minimum Practice Income Guarantee.

[II] Practices that exceed their planned level of achievement of the quality and outcomes framework are guaranteed to be rewarded.

2

Primary care trusts' progress in shaping primary medical services and implementing new arrangements

16 This chapter reports on PCTs' readiness for their new role using evidence from study visits and the PCT and practice nurse surveys. Although the evidence from study sites provides a snapshot from nine places and is not necessarily representative of the NHS as a whole, a number of findings are consistent with other recent research **(Ref. 13)**.

Strategic approach

17 At the study sites visited, the extent to which PCTs were implementing clear strategies varied. Many PCTs were using opportunities to shape general practice using growth monies, PMS contracts, PwSIs and quality frameworks to move toward strategic goals. Some had promoted changes to general practice as part of a wider strategy to develop alternatives to secondary care and to relieve pressure on hospitals. These changes are also reported in the Audit Commission's study of PCTs' role in the redesign of care pathways **(Ref. 14)**.

18 But some PCTs felt powerless to effect real change at a practice level. This sense of powerlessness relates to the history of the PCT and its relationships with general practice. It also relates to PCTs' knowledge of their current position, their vision for the future and ability to use their powers to help get there. There was also variation in the extent to which PCTs used partnerships and networks to work with others to help meet their objectives.

19 All the PCTs visited were taking steps to engage with GPs and practice staff, although the extent of this varied. Three out of nine PCTs performed well, with systematic activity in at least three of the five areas reviewed **(Box B)**.

20 The mechanics of clinician and practice engagement were varied. PCTs reported some reluctance among GPs to participate in the PCT agenda, and GPs expressed doubts about whether it would lead to better services for patients. GPs expressed concerns about their workload and its impact on their capacity to take on an enhanced role with the PCT. Around one-half of practice nurses surveyed reported participating in PCT practice nurse networks, with greater proportions participating in other networks centred on either their profession or their general practices. PCTs need to take account of all the available networks to ensure that they make best use of the opportunities for professional engagement that already exist.

Box B

Achieving strong relationships between PCTs and practices

- A range of regular events at which PCT and practice staff and GPs come together – either using existing mechanisms or bespoke ones as necessary.

- A consideration of both PCT and practice issues on the agenda.

- Not overly dominated by a single organisation's agenda, or by a single professional group.

- Seen as useful and credible by practices and by the PCT and well attended by both parties.

- Strong leadership by, and high priority for, the PCT.

Source: Audit Commission

Operational support

21 PCT study sites were scored according to a range of criteria on the provision of operational support for practices **(Exhibit 5)**.

Exhibit 5

PCT operational support for general practice

The number and range of support activities provided at the study sites was varied.

Criteria for assessing the range of support activities are listed at Appendix 2

Total 9-12
PCT engagement in most or all of the activities identified.

Total 5-8
PCT engagement in some of the activities identified, or was very well advanced in one or two areas.

Total 1-4
PCT engagement in one of the activities or others were in the planning stage.

Study site	A	B	C	D	E	F	G	H	I
Human resources	✓	✓✓	✓✓✓	✓✓	✓✓	✓✓	✓✓	✓✓	✓
Information management and technology	✓	✓	✓	✓✓	✓✓	✓✓	✓✓	✓✓	✓
Premises	✓✓	✓✓	✓	✓✓	✓✓	✓✓	✓✓	✓	✓✓
Prescribing	✓	✓✓	✓✓✓	✓✓	✓✓	✓	✓✓✓	✓✓✓	✓✓✓
Total	5	7	8	8	8	7	9	8	7

Source: Audit Commission study sites
(spring/summer 2003)

22 Of the nine study sites, only one PCT scored highly on virtually all aspects measured. The rest were *'fair'* supporters of general practice. Those providing less operational support were not necessarily those with the least resource overall, or those investing the least. In some cases, they had made a strategic decision that their priorities lay elsewhere, for example, tackling health system deficits and hospital waiting targets.

23 Overall, it was usual for one wte staff member in a PCT to be supporting between three and four practices. The way in which staff were deployed varied, as did the nature of the support activities in place **(Exhibit 6, overleaf)**. PCT staff roles included monitoring general practice provision, supporting practices to bring about change and offering practical help for specific local difficulties. At PCT study sites the median cost of this support was £288,000 per annum. These figures excluded any costs for shared services agreements that the PCT may have had. In discussion with study sites it was evident that shared services provided back office functions rather than support for individual practices.

Exhibit 6

Ratio of general practices to PCT staff dedicated to supporting general practice

Some PCT staff provide support to a large number of general practices.

△ PCT

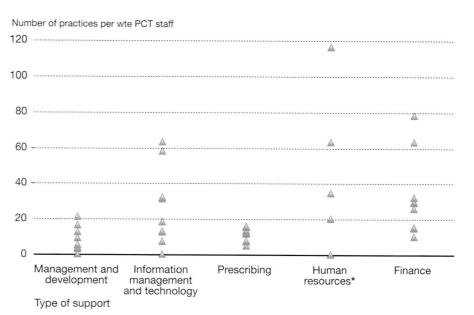

Number of practices per wte PCT staff

Type of support

Note: *At one PCT, one wte staff member supported the equivalent of 250 practices. This value is excluded for clarity

Source: *Audit Commission study sites (spring/summer 2003)*

24 The level of resources for prescribing and for information systems was relatively high. Support for human resources showed the most variation. Finance capacity was stretched, varying from the best resourced PCT, which had one staff member for every 10 practices, to the least resourced, which had one for 78 practices. The average was one wte for 25 practices. This raises questions about PCTs' capacity to support their new responsibilities, for example, contracting with each practice and planning the development of enhanced services and quality and outcomes framework achievements. Although there may be compensating reductions in other functions, such as the administration of family health services (FHS),[l] there is likely to be a mismatch between the skills in place and those needed for the new arrangements.

25 In 2002, auditors appointed by the Audit Commission also raised concerns about management capacity at PCTs and, in particular, the impact of organisational change **(Ref. 15)**. An Audit Commission study of financial management **(Ref. 16)** reports more recent concerns from auditors that over one-third of PCTs have inadequate finance staff and management capacity. Auditors question PCTs' capacity to carry out financial planning to support primary care development, including understanding what money is being spent on, whether value for money is being achieved and how additional investment can be used to improve services. In some PCTs basic financial processes are also an area of concern for auditors.

l   FHS administration includes reimbursement of fees and allowances for GPs; routine functions that will no longer be necessary under the new contractual arrangements.

26 It might be expected that those PCTs with a large number of small practices have more support staff than those with predominantly large practices. Not only do the former have more practices to work with, smaller practices are less likely to have the capacity to improve and develop from their internal resources. Among the nine study sites there was no discernible pattern.

27 The strengths and weaknesses of large and small PCTs, however, were clear. Larger PCTs faced a greater challenge in gathering information on current arrangements in general practice, but their advantage was in providing support services, such as professional human resource services. Smaller PCTs may need to ensure that they form partnerships with others to ensure that such services are provided. Smaller PCTs had closer relationships and more contact with individual practices. Larger PCTs may need to take steps to replicate these close relationships in other ways, for example, through clinical leads and other arrangements for regular contact between practice staff (not just GPs) and the PCT.

28 Lewis et al found that primary care groups (PCG), the predecessor bodies to PCTs, were more effective in giving general practice high priority and in engaging primary care clinicians than PCTs **(Ref. 17)**. They suggest engagement has declined since the inception of PCTs, but that it is needed to ensure that there is a 'bottom up' approach to developing strategy. To facilitate clinician involvement at the larger PCTs visited during this study locality networks of GPs, often on PCG boundaries, had been retained or were in the process of being recreated.

Implementing the new GMS contract and new PMS arrangements

29 The national survey of PCTs was carried out in the autumn of 2003. This was after the ballot in which the profession agreed to the new contract in June 2003, but before detailed guidance, also subject to negotiation, was issued in December **(Ref. 18)**. The results at that time showed that:

- 91 per cent of PCTs said they had an agreed work programme to manage the implementation of the new GMS contract;

- 76 per cent had agreed a programme with practices to discuss how to implement the new GMS contract;

- 81 per cent had held discussions with some or all of their practices on implementing the new GMS contract;

- 37 per cent of PCTs reported that they were *'well or very well prepared'* to implement the new GMS contract (in GMS practices); and

- 41 per cent of PCTs reported that they were *'confident or very confident'* that they will be ready to introduce the elements of the new contract that apply to PMS practices.

30 Respondents identified a number of challenges[l] involved in implementing the new contract **(Exhibit 7)**. There were significant shortfalls in PCT knowledge of key aspects of service organisation and provision – knowledge it is essential for them to acquire if they are to make informed planning and commissioning decisions about services to be provided in general practice in the future.

Exhibit 7

Implementing the new contract – PCTs identified a number of challenges to implementing the new contract*

More than one-third of PCTs identified financial management, responsibility for out-of-hours services and lack of capacity as the main challenges to implementing the new contract.

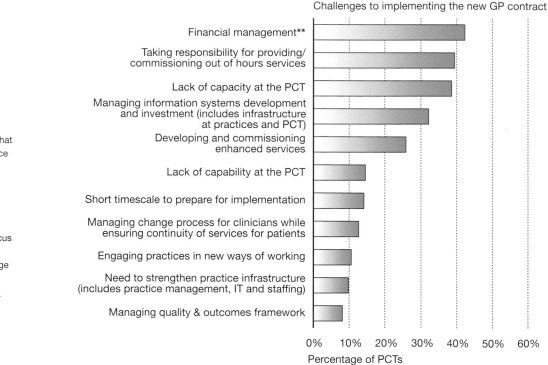

Challenges to implementing the new GP contract

Notes:

*In October 2003 one-half of PCTs reported that delays in publishing the new contract guidance was one of the top three challenges to implementing the contract. Guidance was subsequently published at the end of December 2003.

**Includes perceived lack of resources, understanding funding streams, need to refocus on primary care, costs to PCTs of new arrangements, infrastucture in place to manage contracts at PCT and practices.

Source: Audit Commission national survey of PCTs (October 2003)

31 Nationally, around 40 per cent of practices operate under PMS contracts instead of the 1990 GMS contract. Reasons for this include greater flexibility for the practice, the ability to commission services that more closely meet the needs of under-served populations, and to tackle problems associated with recruiting GPs by offering more flexible options, such as salaried GP positions and nurse practitioners. The national survey of PCTs found that 39 per cent of practices were PMS practices, with wide variation between PCTs. At PCT study sites the proportion of PMS practices ranged from 12 to 80 per cent. Six out of the nine PCTs visited had fair or robust systems in place for monitoring PMS contracts, with most of the key features in evidence **(Box C)**.

l PCTs were asked to identify the top three challenges they faced.

PCTs that have robust monitoring arrangements in place are likely to be in a better position to implement the new GMS contract.

Box C

PCT activities for monitoring PMS contracts at study sites

- Monitoring includes quality of services and financial management of the contract.

- The contract includes flexibility, for example, to adjust funding according to changes in workload.

- Targets for monitoring:
  - were discussed with practices in advance;
  - had a clear rationale;
  - not too many in number;
  - represented a range of practice activities – not just clinical or organisational; and
  - targets could change over time to reflect new priorities, or changing levels of achievement.

- PCTs offer practical help and support to practices to help them to provide monitoring information.

- There is personal contact between PCTs and practices to enable them to discuss monitoring results.

Source: Audit Commission study sites (spring/summer 2003)

---

32 Auditors of PCTs have found that where management capacity was stretched, little or no performance management of PMS practices occurred, even though an agreed framework was in place. Where PMS contracts are well managed, PCTs will be able to transfer what they have learnt to their relationships with other practices. Where they are poorly set up, they pose financial risks to PCTs, risks that may be duplicated in GMS practices if financial control and planning are lacking **(Ref. 19)**.

Service mapping

33 The first step for PCTs to take in developing the sophisticated commissioning arrangements necessary to fulfil their new powers is to carry out service mapping exercises. In particular, since GPs may, in the future, opt out of providing 'additional' and 'enhanced' services, it is key that PCTs are aware of the services that are currently needed and provided. Many PCTs had carried out preliminary mapping activities, but these were by no means comprehensive **(Exhibit 8, overleaf)**. Not surprisingly, where PCTs had mapped service provision, a higher proportion reported being *'well'* or *'very well'* prepared for contract implementation.

Exhibit 8

Mapping 'essential', 'additional' and 'enhanced' GP services

PCTs were well prepared to implement the GP contract where they had mapped service provision.

- ■ Percentage of PCTs 'well prepared'
- ■ Percentage of PCTs 'poorly prepared'

Preparedness of PCTs to implement new contract

Essential services comprehensively mapped
Essential services partially mapped
Essential services not mapped

Additional services comprehensively mapped
Additional services partially mapped
Additional services not mapped

Enhanced services comprehensively mapped
Enhanced services partially mapped
Enhanced services not mapped

0%   10%   20%   30%   40%   50%

Percentage of PCTs responding

Source: Audit Commission survey of PCTs (October 2003)

34 To make decisions about which enhanced services to commission and to judge proposals from practices to provide them, PCTs need to balance their strategic intentions with the desire of practices to offer enhanced services, patient choice, fair access for the population, affordability and value for money. In addition, PCTs need to validate any claims from practices for delivering enhanced services now and, where they are legitimate, they need to make financial provision if they wish to commission them.

Monitoring clinical quality

35 Patient surveys show that patients are highly satisfied with the clinical aspects of their care from general practice, although other research has shown wide variation in clinical quality when compared to best practice **(Ref. 20)**. The quality and outcomes framework sets out standards drawn from the national service frameworks (NSFs)[l] and from other evidence, establishing systems for quality assurance, and an important role for PCTs in monitoring and supporting quality improvements.

36 According to the national survey, only 9 per cent of PCTs do not review practice performance at all. Of those that do, performance reviews are applied to practices with PMS contracts or those GMS practices that are not achieving national targets. Smaller PCTs and those with fewer practices to support were more likely to carry out systematic performance reviews with all practices, perhaps reflecting the scale of the task for those PCTs that have many practices with which to engage.

l NSFs set out standards of service drawn from the best evidence available. Published NSFs include mental health, older people, diabetes, coronary heart disease and renal services.

37 PCTs have mixed views about implementing the quality and outcomes framework. Just over one-half felt *'well prepared'* in this area and nearly one-half felt confident about their capacity to monitor practices. However, 28 per cent of PCTs described lack of data or information as a challenge to contract implementation. At PCT study sites it was the data (both quality and quantity) in relation to quality and outcomes that was of concern.

38 Providing wider access to quality data is one potential driver of quality. The value of comparative quality and outcomes data for practices and PCTs was largely accepted as being helpful at PCT study sites, and most were sharing such data with practices, often identifying practices in such comparisons.

39 Quality and outcomes data for practices (and data quality, for example, on practice lists) will determine payments. It should, therefore, be available publicly on probity and transparency grounds. Patients should have access to information to enable them to exercise informed choice. The public has a right to know about the quality of services and needs assurance that the considerable investment of resources is leading to demonstrable improvements. In publishing such data, PCTs would need to guard against the possible negative impact of 'league tables' on the stability of service provision and morale, and ensure that proper explanatory information was also published to help users to understand the context for the data, including issues such as historic levels of funding.

GP out-of-hours services

40 The PCT survey confirmed the diversity of provision of services,[l] with an average of three out-of-hours service providers in each PCT. A quarter of PCTs reported that they did not know how many practices intended to opt out of providing out-of-hours services, although some practices may not have decided by the time the survey was carried out – October 2003. The notice period for opting out is 9 months so the earliest that all PCTs will assume responsibility is December 2004. Only 7 per cent of PCTs planned to become the sole provider of their own out-of-hours services in the future, compared with 47 per cent that planned to commission services from either existing or new providers, and 36 per cent that will do both. Eleven per cent of PCTs reported that they did not then have any future plans for out-of-hours services.

Improving access – closed lists and assignments

l   GPs may fulfil their current responsibility by providing primary care out-of-hours to their practice populations themselves, by participating in a GP cooperative or by delegation to a commercial provider. NHS Walk in Centres and A&E Departments are open to everyone.

41 PCTs are responsible for ensuring universal access, for example, by making arrangements to ensure that practices are set up or expanded in under-served areas, and by working with practices to avoid closing lists to new patients. Where there are closed lists, not only do patients have less choice of GP, they may not be able to find a local practice that is willing to accept them at all. In these circumstances PCTs

have to assign patients to a list, potentially against the wishes of both the patient and the practice.

42 The new GMS contract introduces a formal and transparent process for list closures whereas previously, GPs could decide whether to close their lists and not to register particular individuals. Under the new contract, if a list is open a practice cannot unreasonably refuse to register new patients. Practices must declare in advance to the PCT their intention to close their list and the proposed closure period. The PCT will discuss what needs to be done to avoid closure. If it is unavoidable the minimum closure period is three months. A practice making this decision will not do so lightly, because of the loss of capitation income and the fact that the PCT will take closure into account when considering any application by the practice to expand services **(Ref. 3)**. These changes will assist practices to manage workload and PCTs to plan services as well as increase transparency for patients.

43 PCTs that took part in the survey reported that 14 per cent of practices' lists were closed. This may under-estimate the extent of the problem, for example, PCT study sites described lists that are closed 'unofficially' or practices that close to certain patients. In addition, 18 per cent of PCTs reported that they did not know how many local practices had closed lists.

44 The data collected from practices suggest that closed lists are not associated with simple proxies of workload, such as the ratio of patients registered with a practice to wte primary care professional or the proportion of elderly patients on the list **(Exhibit 9)**. This supports the view of study site PCTs, and of other commentators, that reasons for list closure are often about localised difficulties in the practice. PCTs need to understand the reasons in order to be able to offer appropriate support.

45 Nationally, 0.5 per cent of the resident population are assigned by PCTs to GPs' lists each year (range 0 to 1.5 per cent at study sites). It can be a significant issue for patients. However, almost one in five PCTs surveyed were not aware of the number of patient assignments in the previous year. In future PCTs must take all available steps to minimise the need for assignment of patients to practices. Patient assignments are not only made when practice lists are closed: sometimes PCTs need to assign patients to lists where relationships between a practice and a patient have broken down (for example, if a patient is violent). It is essential that PCTs are aware of numbers of, and reasons for, assignments and for closed lists, so that they can deliver appropriate solutions.

46 Improving access to primary medical services in small areas with under-supply is sometimes achieved through PCTs commissioning new practices using either PMS or a PCT directly managed service. Overall, numbers of directly managed practices are small: 3 per cent of practices, according to the PCT survey. This approach can only be a solution to closed lists where the population denied access is concentrated in small areas. Where populations are dispersed, supporting existing practices to keep their lists open is the only practical solution.

Exhibit 9

Closed lists and proxy measures of general practice workload

Patients may have difficulty registering with a GP, but the reasons for this are not straightforward.

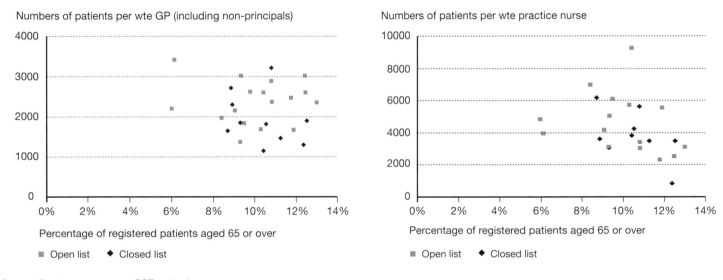

Numbers of patients per wte GP (including non-principals)

Percentage of registered patients aged 65 or over

■ Open list　◆ Closed list

Numbers of patients per wte practice nurse

Percentage of registered patients aged 65 or over

■ Open list　◆ Closed list

Source: *Practice survey at one PCT study site (June 2003). A similar pattern is demonstrated at all study sites*

Improving access – patient experience

47 The main criticisms of general practice emerging from patient surveys relate to access to care, including waiting times to get an appointment, waiting in the surgery, getting through to the practice by telephone, waiting for a hospital appointment and waiting for a visit or appointment out-of-hours. Other access issues that were mentioned include difficulties with surgery hours and difficulties accessing GPs because of other staff, such as receptionists **(Ref. 21)**.

48 PCTs are responsible for ensuring that the targets for all patients to be able to get an appointment with a GP within 48 hours or with another primary healthcare professional within 24 hours are achieved by December 2004. The 2003 milestone of 90 per cent achievement was reached **(Ref. 22)**. Achievement of these access targets is now incentivised in the contract. Whereas in the past PCTs and practices could agree to develop an Advanced Access Programme,[i] the new contract includes 50 points in the quality and outcomes framework **(Ref. 3)**. In addition, until 2005/06 PCTs must also run incentive schemes for improving access as a Directed Enhanced Service. Participating practices with an average list size will receive £2,500 for joining a scheme and a further £2,500 if they acheive a locally agreed level of improvement. Many PCTs and practices will use this to incentivise achievement of the 24/48 hour access target.

i A programme in the Primary Care Collaborative run by the National Primary Care Development Team.

49 The access targets were controversial at study sites: there were concerns that targets can become 'tick box' exercises rather than activities that lead to meaningful quality improvement. While the Advanced Access Programme has reduced delays for patients seeking appointments, there was concern that a heavy emphasis placed on the 24/48 hour access targets had unintended consequences. For example, some practices do not allow patients to book appointments more than 48 hours ahead and this may inconvenience patients, deter them from seeing the doctor or compromise continuity of care with the patient's preferred doctor. Other practices do not operate any appointment system. These practices are not counted in assessing achievement of the target but there may be lengthy waits in the surgery. Not allowing booking more than 48 hours ahead is against Department of Health policy.

50 PCTs have a significant role, not only in monitoring the letter of the targets, but also the spirit of whether patient access to services is improving, seeing the targets as aspects of access, rather than as ends in themselves **(Ref. 23)**.

Improved prescribing

51 Prescribing support was a well-developed area of support to practices at PCT study sites, with seven out of nine providing wide ranging support including: improving prescribing quality via support pharmacists, participation in the Medicines Management Collaborative,[I] and innovations such as supplementary prescribing by pharmacists to improve access. Two-thirds of PCTs in the national survey reported that they commission prescribing support for practices, an average of one wte pharmacist supporting 12.8 practices. In four-fifths of PCTs, these were financed via a 'top slice' from the prescribing budget, although for the other one-fifth, a wide range of financing streams was reported.

52 Financial pressures were common at PCT study sites, with only three out of nine PCTs visited remaining within their budget for prescribing. Prescribing costs have risen significantly and are likely to continue to do so as better, but more expensive, treatments are launched and evidence-based guidance is implemented, the impact of which is to make beneficial treatment available to more patients. Auditors have undertaken local audits of primary care prescribing where managing within budget was identified as an area of financial risk and PCTs have received advice on how to improve in this area **(Ref. 24)**.

I   A programme run by the National Prescribing Centre.

Building the infrastructure of general practice

Primary care clinical workforce

53 The overall level of staffing in practices has the most influence on their capacity to provide patient services. Tackling staffing shortages as the service expands is one of the key concerns of the new contract and of other policy initiatives. Recent data suggest that targets for GP recruitment are being met overall **(Ref. 25)**, although it is likely that this varies from place to place. Increases in headcount alone cannot be translated into a proportional impact on capacity due to the growth in part time working. The Audit Commission's earlier report, for example, showed significant increases in the number of GPs working part-time since 1990 **(Ref. 1)**. More recent data show that between September 2002 and September 2003 the number of GPs in England rose by 457 (1.4 per cent) but the net effect was only 26 wte (0.1 per cent) because of the continued increase in part-time working **(Ref. 26)**.

54 PCTs need to have an overview of the staffing situation, especially given the range of possible flexible working options that are now available. General practice vacancies were a cause of concern to most of the PCTs visited, although not all were aware of current levels. Data from the practice surveys at PCT study sites suggest that vacancies for GPs and practice nurses ranged from 0 to 9 per cent of the workforce. Future retirements were of concern at all the study sites. In 2002, one in three GPs and practice nurses was aged 50 or over and broadly the same profile continued in 2003 **(Ref. 1)**. One-third of practice nurses worked 20 hours or less each week **(Ref. 1)**. There may be potential to increase the working hours of some practice nurses, but this may require the introduction of additional family friendly initiatives and other flexible work options.

55 Recruitment and retention initiatives were also in evidence in four out of nine PCT study sites. Some salaried GPs were employed by 58 per cent of PCTs, with numbers varying greatly from one PCT to another. PCTs are also developing roles for PwSIs, for example, to improve chronic disease management such as diabetes, coronary heart disease and respiratory disease, or as an alternative to a consultation with a hospital consultant, for example, in orthopaedics or dermatology **(Ref. 14)**. Two-thirds of PCTs reported that they had some PwSIs and had planned how they wanted to deploy them. One-quarter had not yet made such plans and 11 per cent reported that they did not have any PwSI. Five out of nine PCT study sites were developing new and expanded roles for nurses and pharmacists in order that they could take on some work traditionally done by doctors.

56 Data from the practice nurse survey show the wide range of tasks and clinics that nursing staff provide **(Exhibit 10, overleaf)** and over half (53 per cent) reported delegating work to health care assistants.

Exhibit 10

Tasks and clinics provided by practice nurses

Practice nurses provide a wide range of tasks and clinics.

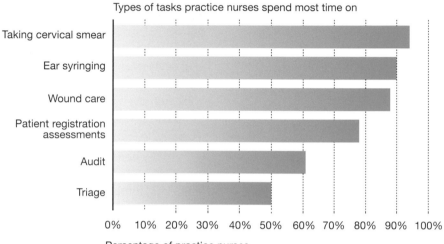

Types of tasks practice nurses spend most time on

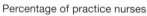

Percentage of practice nurses

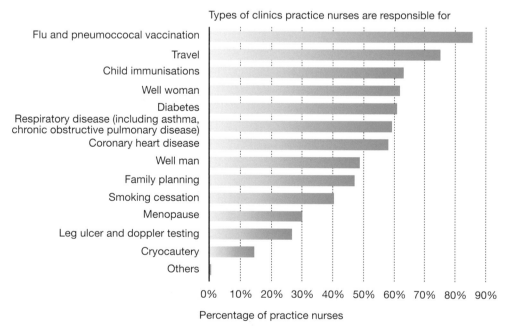

Types of clinics practice nurses are responsible for

Percentage of practice nurses

Source: Audit Commission survey of practice nurses (November 2003)

57 Employing nurse practitioners (registered nurses who diagnose and treat patients) offers the potential for increased substitution of medical staff, but numbers, although growing, remain small, with only 42 wte recorded posts across the nine PCT study sites. This represents less than 5 per cent of practice clinical staff (for example, GPs, nursing staff and physiotherapists), or 10 per cent of registered nursing staff in practices surveyed.

Professional human resources services

58 Systematic processes to ensure that information about current workforce issues is available at PCTs are less well developed, as is the inclusion of human resources within an overall strategic context. PCTs need to take specific steps to ensure that they are in a position to collect information to enable them to build human resources issues into their strategies. Aspects of good human resources practice are required elements of the quality and outcomes framework in the new GMS contract. In addition, as they are employers, practices must fulfil statutory requirements in relation to the employment of their staff.

59 Professional human resources support for general practice was stretched in many of the PCTs with large numbers of practices to support. Some PCTs took the view that human resources within practices *was not the business of the PCT*. The national survey of PCTs found that 72 per cent provided human resources services to local practices. The nature of services, at study sites, varied from systematic support through to a reactive response to one-off problems. Occupational health services were reported to be available for all practice staff in 79 per cent of PCTs, but in the remainder, the services were available to GPs only. Only 42 per cent of practice nurses surveyed had access to occupational health services.

60 Staff appraisal may be one indicator that PCTs can use to identify the practices that may need help in achieving the human resources standards set out in the new contract, standards that aim to assure the quality of services that patients receive. Forty-six per cent of practice nurses reported that they had been appraised in the last 12 months.[I] The same proportion of practice nurses reported taking part in clinical supervision, either on a one-to-one basis with a GP, with another nurse or as part of a peer group.

61 Most practice nurses (90 per cent) reported that they had a contract of employment. Where this was the case, the content of some contracts had significant gaps **(Exhibit 11, overleaf)**, suggesting that some improvements could be made with the support of the PCT. For example, at some PCT study sites practices use a contract template developed by the PCT.

62 The results from the practice nurse survey showed significant access to training **(Exhibit 12, overleaf)**. Three-quarters of practice nurses reported that they had received training in cardiac resuscitation in the last 12 months[II] and one in three had received training about child protection. PCTs can also have a role to play in supporting training initiatives for practice staff, either providing it or ensuring cover for practice staff to attend.

I The standard in the quality and outcomes framework is 100 per cent, with achievement rewarded with two points **(Ref. 3)**.

II The standard in the quality and outcomes framework is that all practice-employed clinical staff should attend training/ updating in basic life-support skills in the preceding 18 or 36 months **(Ref. 3)**.

Exhibit 11

Conditions set out in practice nurses' contracts of employment

Some contracts of employment have significant gaps.

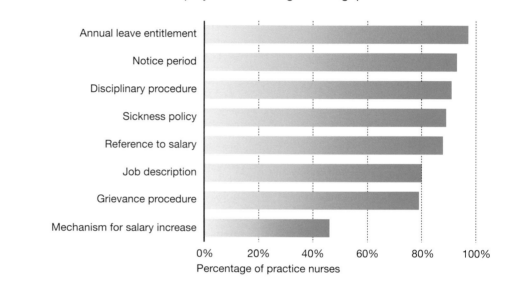

Percentage of practice nurses

Source: Audit Commission survey of practice nurses (November 2003)

Exhibit 12

Practice nurses' access to training

There were significant developments in providing access to training for practice nurses.

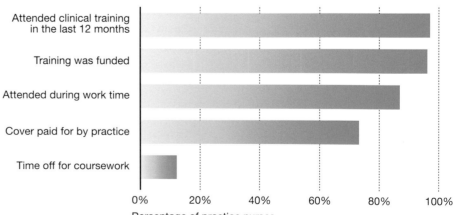

Percentage of practice nurses

Source: Audit Commission survey of practice nurses (November 2003)

Information systems

63 On average, 21 practices at PCT study sites were supported by one wte information services professional, although this varied widely. The study team assessed that five out of nine PCTs supported current information systems well, focusing on a wide range of activities, including stocktakes of infrastructure, development of templates and training support. The aspect of support best developed was the assessment of the information systems infrastructure (six out of nine PCTs). More than two-thirds of the PCTs that responded to the national survey had carried out an information systems inventory in all practices in the previous 12 months. Those who had carried out a complete inventory recently were more likely to describe themselves as *confident to implement the GMS contract* than those who had not.

64 Network connections between practices and the PCT were in place at PCT study sites, with virtually all practices able to communicate with the PCT by email, and widespread access to the NHSnet.[I] Amongst practice nurses, 78 per cent reported access to NHSnet and 74 per cent their own email address. The extent to which such capacity was routinely used or found to be useful varied. In seven out of nine PCT study sites, clinicians in at least three-quarters of practices were able to record patient consultations electronically. Similar numbers of practices routinely received pathology reports electronically. In one PCT, practices were able to check progress of pathology reports on the hospital system.

65 Just over half of practice nurses (55 per cent) reported receiving information systems training in the previous 12 months about clinical software – the area reported at study sites as posing the greatest challenge. One in six had received training in data protection and one in ten in data security.

66 Other aspects of support at PCT study sites related to data quality (for example, Primary Care Information Services (PRIMIS)[II] facilitators to improve data quality in general practice) and assisting practices with templates for clinical systems to help with quality or clinical governance monitoring. The use of the information collected by PCTs was variable and tended to be reactive in relation to what was already routinely collected rather than driven by a proactive consideration of the data that might be needed.

67 PCTs have a vital role to play in making a reality in each general practice of the national information strategy **(Refs.11 and 12)**. Supporting the introduction and full implementation of new systems and ensuring that they are used consistently are major tasks that will require local funding, understanding and motivation.

I The NHS intranet.

II PRIMIS is a free service to primary care organisations to help them improve patient care through the effective use of their clinical computer systems.

Premises

68 In some PCTs, many premises do not meet basic standards. The Audit Commission's earlier report described the current state of GP premises, and reported that 80 per cent were below the recommended size – 14 per cent were judged to be cramped. Nine per cent of premises did not meet basic standards, but this was not evenly spread across the country and London was particularly poorly served **(Ref. 1)**. At PCT study sites, owner-occupation was the most frequent model of premises provision, accounting for around three-fifths of practices in the nine PCTs visited. Overall, around 14 per cent of practice premises had been refurbished at PCT study sites in the last five years.

69 Premises' limitations can be among the most intractable obstacles to securing improvements in primary care, given the lengthy timescales necessary to bring about change. Vehicles, such as Local Improvement Finance Trusts (LIFT)[I], have been introduced and these aim to secure improvements to premises. In the national survey of PCTs in October 2003:

- 46 per cent had made a LIFT bid;

- 85 per cent were made jointly; and

- 84 per cent of bids were successful.

70 There seems to be some confusion among PCTs about eligibility for LIFT and about its potential use. PCTs that had not made LIFT applications gave a variety of reasons:

advised by the strategic health authority…would be unsuccessful

the PCT was unable to quantify revenue implications of introducing LIFT

the PCT lacks capacity and estates expertise

the PCT is not designated a deprived area

71 At PCT study sites few staff were dedicated to premises development. Quality of premises was deemed by PCTs to be good in only two out of nine sites, and it was poor in four. Only two sites had addressed premises as part of their overall strategic direction, though for some, where premises were good or fair, or where there were other equally pressing difficulties that were more readily solved, it was not always the top priority.

72 Under the new contract arrangements, premises development budgets will be held for all the PCTs in the area of a strategic health authority by one PCT.[II] PCTs that are not the lead will need to ensure that they give sufficient attention to identifying the resources needed and supporting implementation.

I Public/private partnerships that enable funds to be raised from the financial markets to invest in primary care premises.

II There are 28 strategic health authorities in England responsible for the performance management of PCTs and NHS Trusts in their area, other than Foundation Trusts.

3

Understanding the use of resources in general practice

73 This chapter reports on the contribution that the Audit Commission's benchmarking tool can make to PCTs' knowledge base about practices, using data collected from more than 200 practices at nine study sites.[I]

Information management requirements

74 PCTs need to gain a better understanding of the health needs of practice populations, funding of practices and the nature of the services delivered. Knowledge about the health needs of practice populations is available from the formula used to calculate the global sum, and this will improve over time. Additional information will be available from GP systems and from the system used to support the quality and outcomes framework, the National Quality Measurement and Analysis System.

75 PCTs need to develop analytical capacity in order to turn relevant data into information and to add this to local knowledge. PCTs can then have informed discussions with practices about issues such as additional services, whether lists can remain open and the standards in the quality framework that can be achieved. For those practices that will gain funds under the global sum, PCTs should encourage service improvements to accompany the increase in resources. In turn, this dialogue with practices should enable PCTs to develop their strategies further.

76 The Audit Commission has developed a benchmarking tool on resource use in practices, tested using data collected from 200 practices at nine study sites. The data collected relates to the 1990 GMS contract or PMS contracts. Although the funds available to practices will change as the new contract comes into operation, PCTs need to understand where funds are deployed now, because the transitional period and the Minimum Practice Income Guarantee for most practices will continue patterns of historic funding for several years. The benchmarking tool will help PCTs to review the way that practices currently use resources, as well as assessing their own capacity to support and develop primary care.

Use of funds

77 As expected, the funds available to general practices within each PCT study site varied widely **(Exhibits 13 and 14, overleaf)**. The median expenditure per registered patient for all practices was £74 and the median for each PCT ranged from £51 to £106. The median cost per consultation was £15.98 with a range for each PCT from £10.71 to £24.67. The most striking feature is the wide variation on both indicators within some of the PCTs.

I   Data are presented for the nine PCTs wherever possible but for one PCT (PCT A) some data were incomplete or missing. Data from this PCT are not shown in some of the exhibits in this chapter.

Exhibit 13

Expenditure on general practice*

Funds available to general practices vary widely with a median of £74 and very wide variations within some PCTs per registered patient.

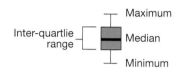

Notes:
*All income sources except premises and prescribing, i.e. Non Discretionary and Discretionary General Medical Services, Personal Medical Services and Hospital and Community Health Services. Inclusion of premises costs changes the numbers but not the extent of variation, for example median expenditure per registered patient including premises costs was £78 and £74 excluding them.

Source: *Audit Commission study sites (spring/summer 2003)*

Expenditure per registered patient

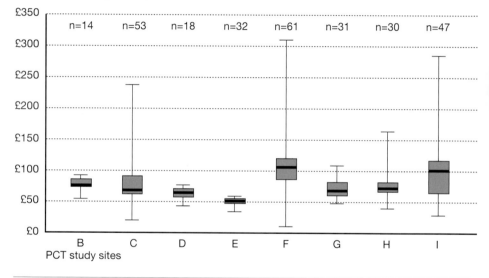

PCT study sites

Exhibit 14

Cost of patient consultations*

Analysing costs in relation to workload also demonstrates wide resource variations, with a median cost of £15.98.

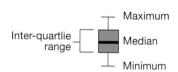

Note:
*Spend from GMS, PMS and PCT staff employed to work in general practices excluding premises' and prescribing costs.

**Patient consultations include those with GPs, practice nurses and other clinical staff.

***One extreme value excluded.

Source: *Audit Commission study sites (spring/summer 2003)*

Cost per patient consultation**

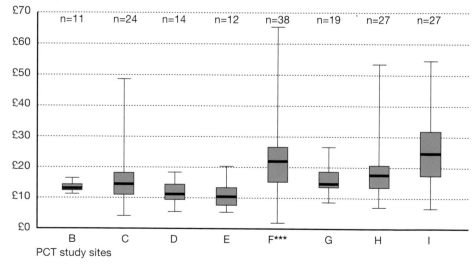

PCT study sites

78 The reasons for variation may include differences in the health needs of practice populations. The cost per consultation indicator may be more responsive to need, as the consultation rate is likely to be higher in areas of high health need as measured by socio-economic proxies. One of the PCT study sites, however, has practice populations with very similar socio-economic profiles, yet very wide variations in spend per registered patient and per consultation. This suggests that the reason for the variation is more likely to be due to the traditional GMS funding regime in which funds followed doctors' investment decisions and not variations in health needs **(Ref. 1)**.

79 The income data have also been analysed by size of practice[I] to assess whether economies of scale explain some of the variation. Analysis shows no association between the size of practice and spend per registered patient or per consultation. In one PCT several practices had GP vacancies and were not drawing down funding. This may account for very low cost per patient and per consultation values (PCT 'F' in Exhibits 13 and 14). Over time, PCTs need to use their powers and influence to secure primary medical services for practice populations on an equitable basis.

Use of staff

80 Staff is the most expensive resource in general practice. It is therefore not surprising that the variation in income available to practices is also reflected in staff ratios. There is wide variation between practices in the number and range of GPs and practice nurses. At the PCT study sites the average number of patients per GP,[II] including non-principals, ranged from 1,720 to 2,183, but within PCTs the range was much wider. The average number of patients per wte practice nurse ranged from 3,885 to 5,202, again, with a wide range within PCTs **(Exhibit 15, overleaf)**.

I One to three GPs, four to five GPs, six or more GPs and registered population.

II Wte, assuming nine sessions is full time, calculated from all sessions in a reference week in mid 2003 for all GPs working in the practice, adjusted for absences, for example, annual leave.

Exhibit 15

Number of patients per WTE GP and practice nurse

There is wide variation between practices in the number of GPs and practice nurses available to provide patient care.

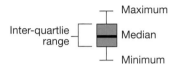

Maximum

Inter-quartlie range — Median

Minimum

Number of patients per wte GP (includes non-principals)*

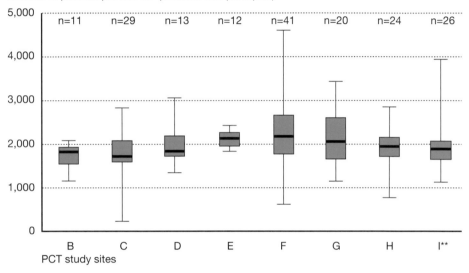

PCT study sites

Number of patients per practice nurse

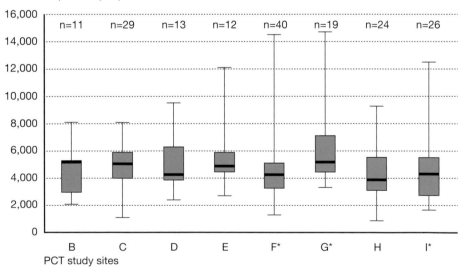

PCT study sites

Notes:
*A GP principal holds the list.

**One extreme value excluded for clarity.

Note:
*One extreme value excluded for clarity.

Source: Audit Commission practice survey (spring/summer, 2003)

Workload

81 Within PCTs, the workload rates of GPs and nurses varied considerably between practices. This was measured according to the number of patients seen **(Exhibit 16)** and the length of consultations **(Exhibit 17, overleaf)**. GPs saw an average of 117 patients per week in their surgeries while practice nurses saw 105. The median

consultation length for GPs was 13.3 minutes and 19.6 minutes for practice nurses, but there was wide variation between practices within PCTs. In order to form a view of the relative workload between practices and to tackle shortages in capacity, PCTs need to understand current patterns of consultation – both in terms of the numbers consulting and the actual consultation lengths.

Exhibit 16

GP and practice nurse consultation rates (per week)

GPs and practice nurses see more than 100 patients each week.

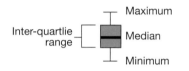

Weekly number of consultations per wte GP (includes non-principals)

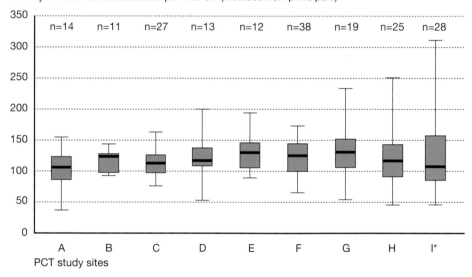

Note:
*One extreme value excluded for clarity.

Weekly number of consultations per wte practice nurse

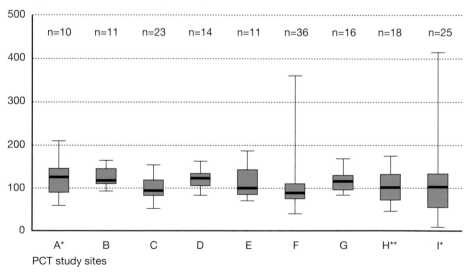

Note:
*One extreme value excluded for clarity.
**Two extreme values excluded for clarity.

Source: *Audit Commission practice survey (spring/summer, 2003)*

Exhibit 17

Length of GP and practice nurse consultations

In a small number of practices GP consultation length exceeded 20 minutes while in nearly half, practice nurse consultation length exceeded 20 minutes.

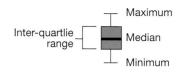

Length of GP (includes non-principals) consultations (minutes)

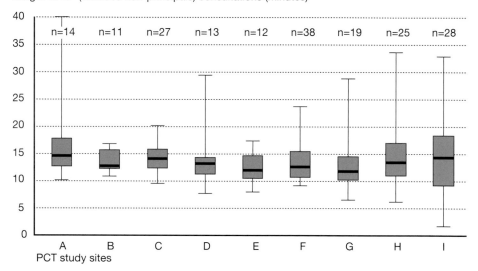

Length of practice nurse consultations (minutes)

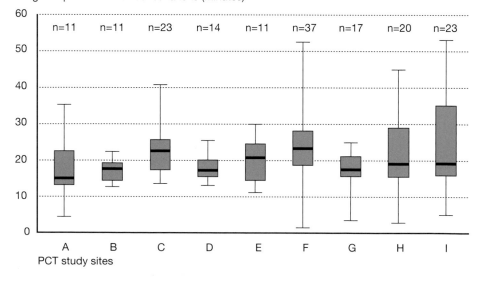

Source: Audit Commission practice survey
(spring/summer 2003)

82 Not surprisingly, the practice data showed that the more consultations per GP per week, the shorter the average consultation time **(Exhibit 18)**.

Exhibit 18

Number of patients seen (per week) and length of consultations

The longer the consultation time, the fewer patients seen.

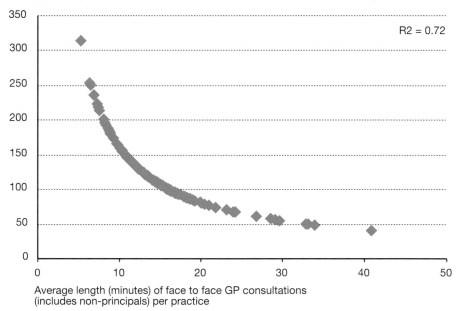

Average weekly number of GP consultations per wte GP (includes non-principals)

Average length (minutes) of face to face GP consultations
(includes non-principals) per practice

Source: *Audit Commission practice surveys (spring/summer 2003)*

Scheduling of appointments

83 Planned consultation intervals of ten minutes were common although actual consultation times were consistently longer than this. On average, 30 per cent fewer patients than anticipated were seen[I], given the planned consultation lengths and session times **(Exhibit 19, overleaf)**. This could not be explained entirely by rates of non-attendance, which averaged only 5 per cent (range 3 to 10 per cent), however, where patients who have booked do not attend, this releases time for some patients to have longer appointments.

84 The findings suggest that ten minute slots do not give patients sufficient time with the doctor. In turn this may introduce delays for other patients and increase pressure in surgeries. Enhancing capacity alone will not have the desired effect unless realistic assessments are made of the number of patients that can be seen in a session, or unless session length is adjusted to reflect the time that patient consultations actually take. The Primary Care Collaborative is supporting practices to help them to understand the volume and nature of demand and to redesign services so that they match demand more closely. Practices that are taking part in the Collaborative report a better match between planned and actual appointment times.

I Range 23 per cent to 42 per cent.

Exhibit 19

Planned and actual consultation lengths

GPs consult with 30 per cent fewer patients than might be expected.

■ Actual
◆ Planned

Weekly number of GP consultations (includes non-principals)

PCT study sites

Source: Audit Commission practice surveys
(spring/summer 2003)

Skill mix in practices

85 Analysis of the skill mix in practices – the ratio of doctors to nurses – demonstrates very wide variation, suggesting that some practices have scope to use nurses more extensively. On average, the wte GP to practice nurse ratio was 2.4:1, but the range for those practices with practice nurses was 1:1 to 34.6:1 **(Exhibit 20)**, variation that was not associated with list size. Five per cent of practices had no practice nurse and these included both small and large practices.

Exhibit 20

Ratio of GPs to practice nurses

Skill mix varied between practices and was not associated with list size.

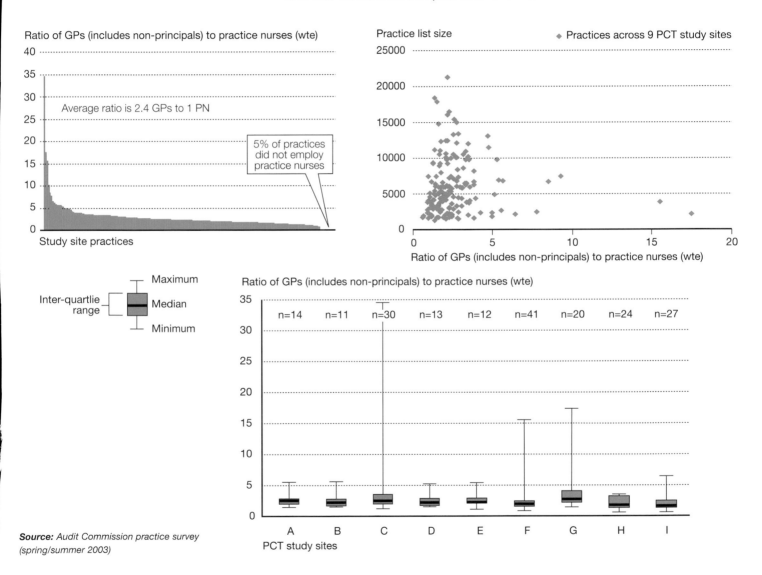

Source: *Audit Commission practice survey (spring/summer 2003)*

4

Making improvements – examples from PCT study sites

86 This chapter describes some of the ways in which PCT study sites were tackling their challenges and responsibilities. It also refers to the support generally available to PCTs to help them to review and improve practice.

Involving practices and primary care professionals

87 Involving and engaging with GPs and other practice staff ensures a mutual understanding of the agenda and that decisions about changing service provision are more appropriate to practice and patient need. Collective commitment of PCT and practice colleagues was being achieved in various ways at PCT study sites **(Case study 1)**.

Case study 1
Involving practices and primary care professionals

Morecambe Bay PCT reported involvement of GPs in many aspects of PCT business, with GP leads in post for information systems and prescribing, and secondment opportunities to enable GPs to work more closely with the PCT. Sessions for this work were funded by the PCT and ensured good communication between GPs and the PCT. Staffing levels in the multi-handed practices enabled colleagues to cover the GPs' absence while they were away on PCT business. In other PCTs, despite attempts to follow this example, high vacancy rates and a large number of single-handed practices made it more difficult to establish a continuous level of GP involvement with PCT activities. The PCT was also focusing much more on engaging with practice managers.

Southwark PCT engaged prescribers in agreeing the targets to be included in the prescribing incentive scheme. All GP and nurse prescribers were consulted on the potential targets via a survey. The results of the survey were presented to the PCT's Medicines Management Group before the set of targets was finally agreed. The survey results were fed back to the prescribers with the finalised prescribing incentive scheme.

North Peterborough PCT supports forums for GPs, practice managers, and receptionists. These are chaired by a member of the PCT primary care team, with the exception of the GP forum, which is chaired by a local GP and attended by the Professional Executive Committee (PEC)[I] with director-level input from the PCT giving a clear signal of the importance of these groups for the PCT's business.

Source: Audit Commission study sites

I   A statutory committee of the PCT, the members of which are clinicians and senior executives.

Improving information management

88 In one study site, all data from multiple sources is being brought together and shared with practices for needs assessment, service review and performance management **(Case study 2)**. The PCT is taking a proactive approach to preparing information systems for the new GMS contract **(Case study 3)**.

Case study 2

Connecting information systems

Solihull PCT plans to 'build' a virtual data warehouse as a way to manage the large, and often disparate, sources of information that exist across the PCT about both the population and practices. Currently, the PCT uses 41 different systems for its many business functions. The data warehouse will provide remote and easy access to centralised data and performance indicators by 'sucking' data out of the multiple systems, such as Exeter[I] and OSCAR,[II] and transforming it into more meaningful information by populating audit and research reports and enabling performance monitoring more generally. The benefits expected include: more accurate information on the health needs of the population and better knowledge of the demand for healthcare services. Such information may contribute to shaping future services or provision.

Source: Audit Commission study site

Case study 3

Preparing information services for the new GMS contract

Solihull PCT decided to take a proactive approach to managing the proposed information systems aspects of the new GMS contract in early 2003. It did this by:

- developing ways to extract information and data from GP systems;
- improving the use of GP systems and the quality of data captured by deploying PRIMIS facilitators;
- exploring the potential to standardise GP computing systems throughout the PCT;
- exploring options for providing support and development of primary care computing more widely, such as assessing the level of information technology skills in practices;
- developing and implementing GP datasets against defined standards;
- defining the reports required to support quality and outcomes;
- beginning work to upgrade GP systems; and
- developing uniform clinical data templates and disease registers in general practice.

Source: Audit Commission study site

I The current system for GMS payments to general practices.

II OSCAR (Online System for Comparative Analysis and Reporting) is a service on NHSnet offering quarterly updated information on all hospital admissions to every provider in England.

Case study 4
PCT managed practice

In April 2002 **North Peterborough PCT** began to manage a split-site practice in one of the more deprived areas of the city. The smallest site had the largest proportion of patients, the majority of whom were from the minority ethnic community. The practice had struggled to recruit GPs, practice management was not used to full advantage and clinical systems were only used for prescribing.

When the senior partner retired, the PCT took over the lease of the practice premises and undertook some refurbishment before the practice moved to purpose-built premises. It trained new practice staff and supported the training and development of existing staff, for example, the practice cleaner was trained as a receptionist. The PCT now employs all the practice staff and has resolved many of the inequities over pay, terms and conditions. All patient appointments are now managed electronically, replacing the parallel systems that had been in place and all patient records are summarised electronically, ensuring that staff use the appropriate clinical systems. In addition the practice is now part of the Primary Care Collaborative working towards Advanced Access.

Source: Audit Commission study site

Commissioning

89 Examples of commissioning activities at PCT study sites included:

- Commissioning a more primary-care-based service, closer to patients' homes, and relieving demand on acute services with ringfenced resources to protect investment. **East Devon PCT**, for example, had mature contracting relationships with the hospital trust and had decided to deliver more services in primary care to reduce the pressure for hospital outpatient appointments and inpatient admissions.

- Commissioning from different service providers, either to improve the patient experience or because existing service providers plan to stop providing the services in question. **Salford PCT**, for example, planned to provide out-of-hours services, with the agreement of local GPs, in order to tackle service deficiencies in the current arrangements. **North Peterborough PCT** provided a service on the retirement of a practitioner **(Case study 4)**.

- Commissioning different services from the same providers in order to better match patients' needs, for example, by conducting enhanced service reviews and ceasing to invest in services that do not meet patient needs and by freeing up resources for other services **(Case study 5)**.

Case study 5
Enhanced services review

Reading PCT conducted an enhanced services review to help it to decide where it should focus its resources in the future. Features of the review included:

- the PCT taking a proactive approach to commissioning (and de-commissioning services);

- anticipation of new planning responsibilities for enhanced services in the new GMS contract;

- trying to ensure greater equity between localities within the PCT; and

- releasing resources to develop or expand services that are considered to be a high priority.

A survey questionnaire was sent to each clinic or service so that they could be involved in the review. Many of these services had grown in an ad hoc way, for instance, following the research or special interest of an individual GP. A report was submitted to the PCT board with recommendations either to retain funding or de-commission. In some cases, funding was retained, but it was recommended that the services seek wider referrals from other practices. The general principle was that existing services should serve more than one practice population and that equity between 'networks' (localities) should be considered. The PCT was guided by the priorities that had been agreed across the six neighbouring PCTs, which worked closely together.

Source: Audit Commission study site

Planning use of resources and delegating budgets

90 The PCT study sites had taken various steps to plan better use of resources, including tackling resource variations. These included:

- working to understand why resources were not always drawn down, for example, if recruitment difficulties meant that GP posts could not be filled, or whether problems with premises were inhibiting the further development. An understanding of these issues and of their impact on overall resources could ensure their importance in discussions about primary care developments;

- agreeing an equalisation policy with practices that enabled differential investment in under-resourced practices over time;

- focusing resources more tightly on the top priority issues, which might result in the withdrawal of funding of lower priority services;

- restricting the growth of the acute sector to enable investment in general practice, ringfencing resources for higher priority primary care projects; and

- working with patient groups and practices to try to support the best use of the resources **(Case study 6)**.

Case study 6
Local team planning

East Devon PCT was devolving powers and resources to local teams, as a means of making resource allocation explicit, and encouraging improved partnership working. Each team included representatives from respective practices, social services, community nursing, community hospitals, the voluntary sector and the PCT general manager for that area.

The teams met regularly and identified common issues and new ways of working together. Ultimately, they planned for budgets to be fully integrated with social services at a local level.

Examples of actions arising from these teams have included the development of a rapid response team to prevent hospital admissions, other integrated health and social services posts and the development of PCT-funded sessional services in practices, where service deficiencies have been identified.

These delegated responsibilities offer practices incentives to innovate and develop new models of service provision. Of vital importance for the PCT however, will be how it continues to monitor the value for money of such innovations.

Source: Audit Commission study site

91 Some PCTs were developing their approach to commissioning to reflect the nature of general practice in their area, for example, where there was a history of strong commissioning from GPs, then greater delegation was possible **(Case study 7)**. Other PCTs were concerned that the infrastructure for greater delegation (including management capacity) was not yet sufficient in primary care. Each PCT must decide what is most appropriate for its local circumstances.

Case study 7
Delegating budgets to practices

East Devon PCT plans to devolve commissioning budgets to GPs, 'building on the best of GP fundholding'. This would be done in the following stages:

* validating data on referrals and emergency admissions from the hospital trust;

* notional activity budgets for each practice are agreed, for example, for routine outpatients and surgery; and

* ultimately, budgets will be devolved to practices for all commissioning decisions, providing incentives for GPs to think about 'alternatives' to referrals.

So far, the PCT has held well-attended evening meetings for GPs; almost one-half have agreed to be involved in the initial validation stage. The PCT has also convened a high-level steering group, including the PCT Chief Executive, to ensure that the project's progress continues.

Source: Audit Commission study site

Improving quality

92 PCTs had taken various steps to improve quality monitoring **(Case study 8)**. Those most appreciated by practices were those that were practical and supportive: examples included support for pharmacists to review effective prescribing practice and help and support for information systems to help monitor clinical practice using computers.

Case study 8
Improving quality

Reading PCT has an incentive scheme, which is part of the PCT's clinical governance quality framework and is also used to inform and monitor PMS contracts (which form the majority). It has the following key elements: prescribing, the NSFs, risk management, health and safety, information systems and public involvement. Some of the areas of focus may change year on year, as achievements and priorities change.

A target is identified for each area. This may be about establishing registers, processes for disease management (for example, risk assessments of patients with diabetes), processes for audit or intermediate outcomes (for example, the proportion of patients with diabetes who have good glycaemic control). For each target, a rationale is given (for example, it is linked to an NSF target, or is a local priority).

There are 15 targets in total. Each one has a point value – practices may achieve a total of 100 points and incentive payments are linked to the points.

The scheme has clear guidance for practices on the sources of information or data required (for example, the Read codes[I]) and who at the PCT can help.

The PCT believes that having had this scheme in place will help them to work with practices to establish systems for monitoring the quality and outcomes framework contained in the new GMS contract.

South Tyneside PCT has a strongly led clinical governance department. As part of its processes, it produces performance indicators for all practices, tailored to practice demography and benchmarked staff costs. These are presented graphically and discussed at each practice's annual facilitated workshop. Progress is reviewed against objectives in order to produce practice development plans. The performance indicators are largely linked to the PCT objectives.

If practices need support, a PCT 'in-reach' practice support team is available. Medical, nursing and practice management support are available through PCT-funded sessions. The personnel forming the support teams are themselves practicing clinicians and are well known and trusted locally.

Source: Audit Commission study sites

93 GPs appreciate practical help and support on prescribing. Good-quality prescribing is in everyone's interest and this was the area that was best supported at the PCT study sites **(Case study 9, overleaf)**. The PCTs involved in this study provided prescribing support in a number of ways, such as:

- providing support pharmacists at every practice for one session per week;

- providing analysis of prescribing data for practices;

- administering prescribing incentive schemes;

- providing pharmacists to undertake medicines management reviews;

- working with other PCTs and with hospital trusts across health economies to agree prescribing protocols and guidelines;

- education initiatives provided by prescribing advisors on new National Institute for Clinical Effectiveness (NICE)[II] or NSF guidance; and

- being involved in the Medicines Management Collaborative.

I   The NHS clinical coding system.

II The NHS body charged with making evidence-based recommendations on new technologies and practice.

Case study 9

Two models of prescribing support

	Morecambe Bay PCT	Solihull PCT
Background	Historically there was only one wte pharmaceutical advisor at the former health authority. The pharmaceutical advisor would attempt to visit all practices once a year to advise on prescribing issues. Gradually, prescribing support pharmacists were employed. One wte pharmaceutical advisor co-ordinates the prescribing and medicines management activity across the PCT.	The PCT has 3.5 wte staff supporting prescribing and medicines management across the PCT; pharmaceutical advisor, prescribing advisor, pharmacy technician and a lead nurse, who supports community nurses on prescribing matters. Sessional pharmacists were established ten years ago, to provide support at practices.
Pharmacists within practices	The PCT now employs 7.2 wte support pharmacists. All of them have been in post for at least three years. The pharmacists support 58 practices and are attached to a practice for half to one day per week.	Sixteen sessional pharmacists are contracted to work by the general practice for one to two sessions per week. They support 32 practices.
Source of funding	The prescribing support pharmacists are funded by top slicing the prescribing budget.	The employment costs for the sessional pharmacists are reimbursed through GMS discretionary funds.
Aims of the role	To deliver improved medicines management and more cost-effective prescribing by: • carrying out prescribing audits; • monitoring prescribing reports from the Prescription Pricing Authority;[I] • carrying out medicines management reviews with patients; • reviewing repeat prescribing; • providing educational support to general practice staff; and • agreeing priorities with practices each year, based on practice priorities, clinical governance targets and the prescribing incentive scheme.	To focus on cost-effective and appropriate prescribing by: • carrying out prescribing audits; • reviewing older peoples' medicines; • helping practices to develop protocols; and • progressing the prescribing incentive scheme. The prescribing advisor and sessional pharmacist meet with the practices bi-monthly to review performance, which is informed by a pro-forma return to the PCT.
Prescribing outcomes	Prescribing expenditure is generally within budget across the PCT, but this masks variation in overspends and underspends between practices. Practices are monitored on achievement of targets set out in the clinical governance programme and the prescribing incentive scheme.	Prescribing expenditure is generally within budget across the PCT, but this masks variation in overspends and underspends between practices. Practices are monitored on achievement of targets set out in the prescribing incentive scheme.

I   The Authority that administers payments for NHS prescriptions and provides advice and management information on prescribing to the NHS.

Source: Audit Commission study sites

Improving access

94 Good engagement and communication between the PCT and practices help PCTs to understand reasons for list closure and take steps to support practices in order to avoid it **(Case study 10)**. For example, in some places, contracts for PMS practices were insufficiently flexible to allow for in-year changes in patient numbers in practice remuneration. This provided an incentive for practices to close their lists when the number of patients reached the number agreed in the contract. In response to this, some PCTs had agreed more flexible contracts that could allow for a certain degree of fluctuation in patient numbers to be reflected in practice reimbursement, hence avoiding this problem. In addition, list sizes will be agreed quarterly in the future, to help avoid the problem arising **(Ref. 18)**.

Case study 10

Improving access

In **Southwark PCT** the number of assignments of new patients to general practices was a real issue in its first year of operation. It was assigning 300 to 900 patients to practices every quarter.

The PCT, through its Patient Advice and Liaison Service (PALS), introduced a new way of assigning patients. PALS receives regular updates on practice list status, that is, whether lists are open or closed. Patients are advised which practices are open and in certain circumstances practices with closed lists will be contacted to see whether they will accept special cases. PALS will keep in regular contact with practices so that information about practice boundaries is maintained. Assignments should only be used as a last resort.

The PCT also encourages practices to keep their lists open by reviewing the per capita element of practice remuneration of all practices each month.

The main benefit for patients was fewer closed lists and an improved service for those seeking to register with a GP. It has also resulted in a 40 per cent decrease in the number of assignments by the PCT and less frustration among patients who are trying to register with a GP.

North Peterborough PCT is a designated cluster area for asylum seekers. Two PMS practices agreed to accept registrations from this group of people. However, the practice lists were soon full, with approximately 1,300 new patients. The practices struggled to keep their lists open to new patients due to the additional workload and staff turnover.

The PCT wants to provide support to these practices, as well as ensuring that all patients get access to primary medical services. The PCT supports one of these practices to act as an induction centre for general practice services, that is, to manage all new-patient screening and provide any necessary treatment. After six months – the time at which asylum seeker consultation rates with GPs are generally thought to be similar to the resident population – most patients would be invited to register with another practice for continuing services. Only those patients with long-standing problems would remain registered with the general practice acting as the induction centre. In the event that assignment becomes necessary, all practices would be on a rota to receive assigned patients to maintain equity of workload.

North Peterborough PCT established and funded a 'violent' patient scheme. Patients who are violent, or who threaten violence, towards practice staff are referred into the scheme for six months. Patients are notified when these arrangements are put in place. If patients need primary medical services then they must attend the police station to see one of four police surgeons. Full medical records are available to the police surgeons. GPs are said to value the scheme. Patients have a right of return to 'normal' general practice services after six months, but will be assigned to a practice different from their original one. In its first year of operation eight patients have been referred to the scheme.

Source: Audit Commission study sites

Developing the workforce

95 This report has already described wide variation in staffing levels, scope for greater use of non-medical professionals and varying views among PCTs on human resources responsibilities. The following examples are from PCTs which saw workforce issues as one of their key primary care development responsibilities **(Case study 11)**.

Case study 11
Support for good practice in human resources

Morecambe Bay PCT has made general practice human resources an integral part of its business. It has developed a proactive human resources service in order to support practices. The PCT funds the human resources service to practices. Strategically, human resources implications are considered an integral part of the development of strategies for services. Operationally, a service is provided that is tailored to the general practice working environment, and includes:

- help with recruitment and selection;
- good employment practice in job design, short listing and interviewing, and contracts of employment;
- help with induction of new employees;
- provision of advice and support on terms and conditions and employment legislation;
- help with discipline and grievance procedures and with fair termination of employment;
- advising on performance and capability issues;
- helping practices with training and development plans, and helping them to find cost-effective ways to implement them;
- providing team development opportunities for general practice, helping to break down professional barriers and improve partnership working; and
- provision of health and safety advice and support.

South Tyneside PCT had established 'Career Start' posts for GPs to help recruitment. These posts enable GPs to move into the area without them committing to partnership in a particular practice immediately. They also had a well developed nursing strategy that considered nursing roles strategically. It included the development of nursing roles and skills at all levels, the potential for substitution with healthcare assistants and, therefore, how these skills might be developed.

The PCT has developed a practice management support team. This is staffed by known and respected practice managers from the local area, who in turn can draw on the assistance of other members of the PCT as necessary. This ensures comprehensive support to local practices delivered by experienced practice managers from within South Tyneside. This assistance is provided to any practice requesting help, and delivered on their premises. This helps to develop practice ownership of any solutions generated by the support team.

Morecambe Bay PCT employed three part-time practice nurse facilitators for 11 to 15 hours per week to support practice nurses. The local Workforce Development Confederation provides the funding for these posts and is equivalent to one wte. The facilitator's role is to:

- promote and find placements for practice nurses and nurse practitioner trainees;
- pull together the general training and development needs of practice nurses and ensure that progress is made in meeting these needs;
- act in an advisory capacity to practice nurses on issues that arise within general practice; and
- plan the PCT-wide practice nurse forum meetings that are held twice a year and are used to discuss issues, such as the implications for practice nurses of the paper, *Liberating the Talents* **(Ref. 10)**. These meetings provide the only opportunity for all practice nurses to get together.

North Peterborough PCT established a peripatetic practice team called the 'Parachute Team'. The team comprises one full-time GP, two full-time specialist nurses and 1.6 wte health care assistants and a half-time outreach worker. The aim of the team is to help practices to improve access to general practice services for all patients, particularly those who find it most difficult, such as those from minority ethnic groups, asylum seekers, the homeless and travellers.

If a practice wants to use the services of the Parachute Team they need to apply to the PCT, who then meet with the practice to agree a 'contract' of engagement. The role of the Parachute Team is clarified with practice staff, as is their role in resolving any issues that may arise.

The Team will be 'parachuted' into a practice to take over from the practice staff and carry out their clinical work while the practice staff take time out to consider their own solutions for improving access. The Parachute Team also acts in an advisory role and helps to facilitate change where it is needed.

Source: Audit Commission study sites

96   There are many sources of information and guidance available to help PCTs review and improve practice **(Box D)**.

Box D

List of websites providing information and support for PCTs

General

www.modern.nhs.uk

The NHS Modernisation Agency was established to support the NHS and its partner organisations in modernising services and improving patient experiences and outcomes. It is the umbrella agency for the National Primary and Care Trust Development Programme (NatPaCT) and the National Primary Care Development Team (NPDT).

www.natpact.nhs.uk

NatPaCT was established following publication of *Shifting the Balance of Power in the NHS*. It provides organisational development support to PCTs.

www.npdt.org

The NPDT Team supports a number of programmes, such as the National Primary Care Collaborative and the National Falls Collaborative, which aim to help practices and organisations develop transferable skills in quality improvement.

Prescribing

www.npc.co.uk

The National Prescribing Centre is an NHS service that facilitates the promotion of high quality, cost-effective prescribing and medicines management.

www.ppa.org.uk

The Prescription Pricing Authority provides a secure, high quality prescribing and dispensing information service as well as managing the payments for prescription items

Premises

www.nhsestates.gov.uk

NHS Estates is an executive agency of the Department of Health and provides expert advice, information and guidance on estates and facilities management and supports the delivery of modern healthcare premises.

www.primarycare.nhsestates.gov.uk

This website identifies the key considerations and actions for those involved in the planning, briefing and design of primary and social care premises. It also gives some guidelines on funding, procurement and design.

Staff

www.rcgp.org.uk/qtd/whatis.asp

The Quality Team Development is an initiative developed by the Royal College of General Practitioners (RCGP) which offers a supportive approach to clinical governance. It enables primary care organisations (PCOs) and primary health care teams to identify developmental needs and also facilitates the sharing of good practice within the PCO.

nGMS and PMS contracts

www.doh.gov.uk/gmscontract

This site provides information about the new GMS contract and access to relevant guidance.

www.doh.gov.uk/pmsdevelopment

This site provides information about PMS and access to relevant guidance.

www.natpact.nhs.uk/primarycarecontracting

Support to Practices and PCTs on new GMS and PMS from the NHS Modernisation Agency and the NPCDT.

Patient choice

www.doh.gov.uk/waitingbookingchoice/pcaccess.htm

The site provides information on changes within the NHS to reduce waiting times for treatment and to offer choice about when and where patients receive treatment. Waiting, booking and choice is part of the wider NHS strategy to give patients fast convenient access to health and social care services, including primary care.

Benchmarking

www.audit-commission.gov.uk/pcts

This site contains the benchmarking tool on resource use in general practices and a tool for PCTs to assess their own capacity to support and develop primary care.

Source: Audit Commission

- perceived confidence and preparedness to implement the contract; and
- whether PCTs had mapped general practice services.

Survey of practice nurses in England

In collaboration with the Royal College of Nurses, a three-page questionnaire was sent to the home addresses of 2,000 registered nurses who lived in England and were members of the RCN Practice Nurse Forum. A letter of endorsement from the General Secretary of the RCN accompanied the questionnaires. The survey form asked for information on:

- current employment;
- clinical and personal development;
- terms and conditions of employment;
- use of information systems at work;
- prescribing; and
- clinical responsibilities.

By the close of the survey, 1,065 questionnaires had been returned. This represents a simple response rate of 53 per cent. Excluding questionnaires returned as undeliverable by the post office and those returned as inappropriate by the recipient, the useable response rate was 49 per cent.

The Audit Commission is grateful to the RCN for their help with the organisation of the survey.

Appendix 2: Study sites

1 Main study site PCTs

The study team visited nine PCTs to gather data and information about resource use in general practice. In addition, we surveyed 372 practices across the study sites and made short visits to several practices. The study methodology is described in Appendix 1.

The main study sites were:

- Barnet PCT;
- East Devon PCT;
- Morecambe Bay PCT;
- North Peterborough PCT (now part of the Greater Peterborough Primary Care Partnership);
- Reading PCT;
- Salford PCT;
- Solihull PCT;
- South Tyneside PCT; and
- Southwark PCT.

We are grateful to all the staff at these PCTs and to their general practices for their help with compiling data and for spending time talking to the team.

2 Other sites

In addition to the main study sites, short visits were made to several PCTs to help with the early development of the study. These PCTs were:

- Brighton and Hove City PCT;
- Halton PCT; and
- Hillingdon PCT.

Thanks are due to the staff at these PCTs for the time they spent with members of the team.

John Oldham, Head of National Primary Care Development Team, NHS Modernisation Agency

Veena Raleigh, Assistant Director, Research & Information, Commission for Health Improvement

Martin Roland, Director National Primary Care Research & Development Centre, University of Manchester

Yvonne Savage, Community and District Nursing Association

Jo Setters, Commission for Healthcare Audit and Inspection Transition Team

Sue Skewis, Professional Adviser, Chartered Society of Physiotherapy

Elizabeth Smith, Community Practitioners and Health Visitors Association

Peter Smith, Chairman, National Association of Primary Care

Michael Sobanja, Chief Officer, NHS Alliance

Kieran Sweeney, Commission for Health Improvement

Rob Webster, Programme Director, GMS & PMS Contract, Department of Health

Cathryn Williams, Formerly Head of Business, London Borough of Barking & Dagenham Social Services

Ian Williamson, Chief Executive, Sefton PCT

Diana Whitworth, Chief Executive, Carers UK

Lynn Young, Primary Care Officer, Royal College of Nursing

Acknowledgements

The study team comprised Beverley Fitzsimons, Tara Lamont, Lucy McCulloch and Gabby Smith under the direction of Wendy Buckley. Sonia McKenzie provided secretarial support.

The Audit Commission is grateful for help and guidance during the course of this review. Responsibility for the contents and conclusions of the report rests solely with the Audit Commission.

References

1 Audit Commission, *A Focus on General Practice in England*, Audit Commission, 2002.

2 *Health and Social Care (Community Health and Standards) Act 2003*, The Stationery Office, 2003.

3 The NHS Confederation, *New GMS contract 2003, Investing in General Practice*, The NHS Confederation and BMA, London, 2003.

4 Department of Health, *Primary Care Trust Revenue resource Limits 2003/04, 2004/05, 2005/06 (HSC 2002/012) and Exposition Tables 2003-6*, Department of Health, 2002.

5 Department of Health, *Shifting the Balance of Power*, Department of Health, 2002.

6 Department of Health, *The NHS Plan: A Plan for Investment, A Plan for Reform*, Department of Health, 2000.

7 Department of Health, *Delivering the NHS Plan*, Department of Health, 2002.

8 Department of Health, *Agenda for Change – Modernising the NHS Pay System*, Department of Health, 1999.

9 Department of Health, *Improving Working Lives*, Department of Health, 2000.

10 Department of Health, *Liberating the Talents: Helping PCTs and nurses to deliver the NHS plan*, Department of Health, 2002.

11 Department of Health, *Information for Health – An Information Strategy for the Modern NHS*, 1998-2005, Department of Health, 1998.

12 Department of Health, *Delivering 21st Century IT Support for the NHS – National Strategic Programme*, Department of Health, 2002.

13 Roland, M and Smith J. *The Role and Contribution of Primary Care Trusts to Quality Improvement in Leatherman S and Sutherland K (eds) The Quest for Quality in the NHS: a mid-term Evaluation*, Nuffield Trust, 2003.

14 Audit Commission, *Quicker Treatment Closer to Home: primary care trusts' success in redesigning care pathways*, Audit Commission, 2004.

15 Audit Commission, *Achieving the NHS Plan: Assessment of Current Performance, Likely Future Progress and Capacity to Improve*, Audit Commission, 2003.

16 Audit Commission, *Financial Management in the NHS*, Audit Commission, 2004. [in production].

17 King's Fund, Lewis R. et al *Future directions for Primary Care Trusts*, King's Fund, 2003.

18 Department of Health, *Delivering Investment in General Practice: implementing the new GMS contract*, Department of Health, 2003.

19 Audit Commission, *Personal Medical Services: A Bulletin for PCT Chairs and Chief Executives*, Audit Commission, 2003.

20 Campbell et al, *Identifying predictors of high quality care in English general practice*, British Medical Journal, Vol 323, 2001, pp 784-7.

21 National Centre for Social Research, *National Survey of NHS Patients – General Practice*, National Centre for Social Research, 2002.

22 Department of Health, *Chief Executive's report to the NHS*, Department of Health, 2003.

23 Audit Commission, *Targets in the Public Sector*, Audit Commission, 2003.

24 Audit Commission, *Primary Care Prescribing: A Bulletin for Primary Care Trusts*, Audit Commission, 2003.

25 Department of Health, *Government on target for GP numbers*, Press Release 2003/0393, Department of Health, 2003.

26 Department of Health, *Statistics for General Medical Practitioners in England: 1992-2002*, Department of Health, 2003.